i-SPY

seaside challenge

DO IT! SCORE IT!

Published by Collins
An imprint of HarperCollins Publishers
Westerhill Road, Bishopbriggs, Glasgow G64 2QT
www.harpercollins.co.uk

HarperCollins Publishers
1st Floor, Watermarque Building, Ringsend Road, Dublin 4, Ireland

A catalogue record for this book is available from the British Library.

ISBN 9780008529789

Printed in Bosnia and Herzegovina

10 9 8 7 6 5 4 3 2 1

Text by Heather Ryce
Front cover image © Coatesy/Shutterstock.com
All internal images © Shutterstock.com except p25 (Sea beech) © Zoonar GmbH / Alamy Stock
Photo, p25 (Red rags) © Premaphotos / Alamy Stock Photo, p25 (Mermaid's tresses) © blickwinkel /
Alamy Stock Photo, p33 (Springtails) © Nigel Cattlin / Alamy Stock Photo, p39 (Olive squat lobster)
© WaterFrame / Alamy Stock Photo, p75 (Porbeagle shark) © Doug Perrine / Alamy Stock Photo,
p91 (Tidal power) © Steve Morgan / Alamy Stock Photo.

MIX
Paper from
responsible sources
www.fsc.org **FSC™ C007454**

i-SPY

seaside challenge

DO IT! SCORE IT!

Contents

Tick off each activity as you do it!

How to use this book

Get ready to take on the i-SPY challenge with 50 activities to get closer to nature!

Once you've done each activity tick it off on the contents list. You can do them in any order you like.

Note to grown-up:
Join in the fun by doing the activities together and supervise any that you feel necessary.

Look out for activities which have eco points. These are awarded for doing something that helps look after the planet and its wildlife. Once you score 200 eco points, send off for your i-SPY eco-hero certificate and badge.

As well as activities, the book is packed with facts, photos and things to spot. If you spy it, score it by ticking the circle or star. Items with a star are difficult to spot so you'll have to search high and low to find them. Once you score 1000 spotter points, send off for your i-SPY super-spotter certificate and badge.

How to get your i-SPY certificates and badges

✓ Ask a grown-up to check your score.

✓ Apply for your certificate and badge at collins.co.uk/i-SPY (if you are under the age of 13 you'll need a parent or guardian to do this).

✓ We'll send you your certificate and badge!

Build a giant sandcastle

Sandy beaches are the most common type of beach and form due to flowing water in rivers and streams eroding the land – they are also the best type of beach for building your own giant sandcastle!

You'll need:

different-sized buckets, spade, items to decorate your castle (flags, shells etc.), water

What to do:

1 To help you build the perfect sandcastle, add water to a full bucket of sand or pick a spot to build where the sand is cool and damp.

2 Make sure the tide will stay out in the area where you build. You don't want your hard work to be washed away halfway through.

3 Using your spade, outline the area where you want to fit your castle.

4 Fill your buckets with sand and quickly flip them over. Tap the bucket with your spade and remove it slowly each time to help keep the castle shape.

5 Use your smaller buckets to create turrets on top of larger sandcastles.

6 Fill the area you mapped out and decorate your castle so it is fit for a king or queen!

Add a moat to your sandcastle

What to do:

1 Dig a trench with your spade or your hands around your castle.

2 Use your bucket to fill your moat with water.

3 To finish, build a wall of sand around your moat to protect it.

See if you can spot any of these nearby:

Beach towel — 5 POINTS

Deck chair — 5 POINTS

Sunglasses — 5 POINTS

Ice cream — 5 POINTS

Gull — 5 POINTS

Seaweed — 5 POINTS

Shell — 5 POINTS

Boat — 10 POINTS

Lifeguard — 10 POINTS

2

Get creative in the sand

In the UK you are usually only within a two-hour drive of a beach. Isn't that great? Beaches change every single day with the tide bringing in new material, and removing others.

If you find yourself at the beach without a bucket and spade there are still lots of ways to have fun with the sand. Just get creative!

Make a sand angel

Just like in snow, you can use your body to make the outline of an angel in the sand.

What to do:

1. Find a patch of the beach with clean, soft sand.

2. Lay down on your back and, with your arms and legs straight, move them up and down and in and out.

3. Stand up and view your angel in the sand – why not decorate it with shells or feathers? Or write your name beside it using a stick?

Cover yourself or someone else in sand

Lying long enough to be covered in sand can be a great test of your self-control. Can you stay still long enough to be completely covered in sand?

What to do:

1 If burying someone else, ask them to lay on their back on an area of the beach with soft sand.

2 Start by covering their feet and legs, letting them get used to the weight and texture of the sand on their body. Use your hands to scoop up large handfuls of sand.

3 Cover them with sand all the way to their shoulders, making sure their face and head are always clear.

4 Why not use your imagination and mould the sand into a mermaid's tail around their legs or decorate the mound of sand on top of them with items found on the beach?

5 Take a picture of your hard work.

6 When you are both ready, watch as the person covered in sand attempts to burst free.

Make a shell necklace

Shell necklaces make beautiful pieces of jewellery and can be a great keepsake to remember your day at the beach.

You'll need:

bucket, towel, string, scissors, camera, drill, different sized shells

What to do:

1 Take a walk along a sandy beach at low tide and look for shells lying on top of the sand or half buried.

2 Collect the ones you like in a bucket and when you have enough, give them a clean in sea water and then lay them on a towel to dry in the sun.

3 Cut a piece of string using your scissors to the length you want your necklace to be.

4 Ask an adult to drill a small hole in the shells you want to thread onto the string.

5 When you have added your shells tie the two pieces of string into a secure knot.

6 Take a selfie with your new piece of beach bling!

If you find an animal living inside a shell you have picked up, score 20 eco points for returning it to a nearby rock pool.

20 ECO POINTS

12

There are many different shells that wash up on our beaches. Can you spot all of these?

Cockle

Cockles are one of the most common shells found along the beach. They are small, saltwater clams with shells that close together to protect the animal inside.

5 POINTS

Mussel

Like cockles, mussels are known as bivalves, due to the two shells that close together. You may only find one of the shells due to them breaking apart.

10 POINTS

Whelk

Whelks are carnivores and often eat mussels. They have spiralled shells which vary in size and shape.

15 POINTS

Scallop

Unlike mussels and clams, which attach on to rocks and don't move, scallops swim through the water by opening and closing their shells.

TOP SPOT!

20 POINTS

4

Visit a lighthouse

A lighthouse is a building or tower that helps boats navigate through the dark and warns them of dangers such as large rocksnearby.

Lighthouses have been around for thousands of years and have kept sailors safe when coming to shore in dark or stormy weather. Many old lighthouses are still standing today and are worth a visit.

Lighthouse keepers used to work the light at the top of the tower, pointing it in the right direction to help boats and ships see clearly to shore. However most lighthouses now work automatically. Some have even been turned into hotels!

What to do:

Ask a grown-up to help you research lighthouses near you to visit. You can even go inside some lighthouses and have a look around!

Keep an eye out for these spots when you visit a lighthouse...

Large rocks at sea

5 POINTS

Stormy seas

10 POINTS

Lighthouse hotel

10 POINTS

Fishing boat

10 POINTS

Red and white lighthouse

10 POINTS

Lighthouse with light on

20 POINTS

5

Skim a stone

Skimming stones can be a tricky skill to master, but with lots of practice and a steady arm you will get the hang of it.

You'll need:

a calm day when the sea is still, some flat, smooth stones

What to do:

1 Take a stone and, using your dominant hand, hold the stone out between your thumb and first finger with the rest of its weight lying on your second finger.

2 When you have it balanced, pull your hand and wrist back, before quickly flicking it forward and releasing the stone.

3 You are aiming to spin the stone out in front of you in a straight flat line towards the water. Sometimes it helps to bend down so you are more in line with the surface of the water.

4 If you have aimed correctly, the stone should hit the water and bounce across the surface, leaving ripples in its wake.

5 Once you have it mastered, you can have a competition with your friends or family – who can skim their stone for the most bounces across the water?

Draw a picture in the sand

After heavy rain at the beach, or at low tide, the sand will be wetter than usual. It's a great time to guess what animals have visited by looking at the tracks left behind. You can also create pictures in the wet sand, which will work better than trying to draw them in dry, soft sand.

You'll need:

a sturdy stick, shells/feathers/stones, camera, your imagination

What to do:

1 When the weather starts to get better and the tide is low, make your way to the beach and search for a sturdy stick to use to draw your picture in the sand.

2 If you can, start your drawing from the inside out – that way you can remove any footprints as you go.

3 Use items found on the beach, like shells and stones, to decorate your drawing.

4 Sign your drawing by using your stick to write your name in the sand.

5 Take a picture before the tide comes back and returns the sand to a blank canvas once more.

17

Explore rock pools

When the tide goes out, small pools of seawater and some sea creatures are often left behind. The time when the tide is out is a fantastic opportunity to explore these rock pools and discover what animals and plants are living there.

You'll need:

clear containers filled with sea water, small fishing net, magnifying glass, sturdy shoes, notepad and pen/camera

What to do:

1. Wait until the tide retreats and, with an adult, make your way down to the beach with all your rock pool equipment. Wearing rubber-soled shoes is recommended as the rocks on the beach can be slippery when wet.

2. Once you have found a rock pool gently use your net to fish out animals and plants. Be very careful transferring animals from your net to your plastic container.

3. Use your magnifying glass to take a closer look at what you find.

4. Record your findings before putting everything back into the rock pool.

Score 20 eco points for removing any litter or plastic from rock pools and putting it in a bin.

20
ECO
POINTS

Some animals and plants in rock pools are obvious to see but some are harder spots if they keep themselves hidden.

Barnacles

5 POINTS

Barnacles are tiny animals typically found attached to rocks. Use your magnifying glass to take a good look without disturbing them.

Shore crab

Found in a range of colours from brown to green and black, these crabs tend to scuttle away quickly when disturbed.

10 POINTS

Shanny

This fish is a common spot in rock pools all over the UK. They are quite shy, usually hiding under rocks or in between seaweed, but they can also bite, so watch your fingers!

10 POINTS

Starfish

Another common sight in rock pools, this strange animal feeds on mussels and clams, using its five arms to prise open the shells.

20 POINTS

Sea anemone

Sea anemones may look like plants, but they are in fact animals which are related to jellyfish. It's best not to touch them as they can give you a nasty sting.

20 POINTS

Go dolphin and whale watching

Larger marine mammals, like whales and dolphins, visit UK coastal waters during summer months. Many can be seen from shore, but you could also take a boat trip out to sea.

You'll need:

warm clothes,
sun cream,
binoculars,
camera

What to do:

1. Research good places to go dolphin and whale watching and visit when you expect the weather to be good. Hotspots include Cornwall, the Moray Firth, Shetland and Orkney.

2. If you go on a boat trip, wrap up warmly. Even if it is a nice day, out at sea the temperature is a lot cooler.

3. Wear sun cream as you will be out in the open for a few hours with no shelter from the sun.

4. Use your binoculars to look out for fins breaking the surface of the water – the first sign that a dolphin or whale is swimming nearby.

5. Look out for flocks of seabirds too. They are attracted by fish, and where there are fish, there may be dolphins and whales too.

Score 30 eco points for finding out about the threats facing whales and dolphins, and thinking about three ways you could help protect them.

30
ECO
POINTS

Dolphins and whales belong to an order of mammals known as cetaceans. Like all mammals they give birth to live young and breathe air, so even though they live in the water they are definitely not fish! How many species can you spot?

Bottlenose dolphin

Large and small pods can be seen all round the UK coastline. These animals love to swim, play and surf waves alongside boats.

20 POINTS

Orca

The UK's only resident killer whales can be seen in waters around Cornwall. Despite their name, they are actually the largest members of the dolphin family.

TOP SPOT!

30 POINTS

Minke whale

This species is the UK's smallest whale, and its curious nature sees it hanging around boats quite often.

20 POINTS

Fin whale

Like the minke, they have plates that hang inside the mouth which they use to filter feed krill from the water. The fin whale can mostly be seen off the coast of Scotland.

TOP SPOT!

30 POINTS

Go snorkelling

Snorkelling isn't just a fun way to discover wildlife in coastal waters and connect with nature, it is also a great way to stay fit. This activity is enjoyed best at the height of summer when the water temperature rises.

You'll need:

mask and snorkel, flippers or old trainers, wetsuit

How to stay safe snorkelling:

- Check the current – throw a stick into the water to see how quickly the water is moving and check that there are no obstacles in your way or hidden below the surface before jumping in.

- Stay warm – always check the water temperature before diving in and wear a wetsuit to stay warm if you need to.

- Stay away from algae – blue-green algae can irritate eyes and cause sickness if swallowed.

- Never swim alone – always swim in pairs or small groups and make sure a grown-up can always see you.

Score 20 eco points for snorkelling responsibly – don't touch the sealife or disturb its habitat.

20 ECO POINTS

The fun thing about snorkelling is that you can get close to fascinating sea creatures. When snorkelling can you spot...?

Spider crab

This large crab ranges in colour from orange to red and brown. It can be found amongst seaweed and in between rocks.

20 POINTS

Sea hare

This marine slug is found in rock pools and shallow waters. It is thought that a sea hare's colour depends on the colour of seaweed it eats.

10 POINTS

Sunstar

This large, predatory starfish looks like the Sun with 10-12 short arms and is commonly found in UK waters.

10 POINTS

Ballan wrasse

There are over 600 species of wrasse all over the world, but the ballan wrasse are the biggest and most common in the UK.

10 POINTS

Seahorses can change in colour to match their environment or when performing a courtship dance. They are protected and if spotted should be left undisturbed.

Spiny seahorse

TOP SPOT!

30 POINTS

Forage for seaweed

Despite its name seaweeds aren't a type of plant, but a species of algae. There are over 9,000 different kinds of seaweed of varying size and colour.

Seaweed is used as a food source, in fertiliser, in medicine and has even been turned into environmentally friendly items of clothing.

You'll need:

sturdy shoes, bucket, camera

What to do:

1 The best time to forage for seaweed is when the tide is low – you'll be able to spot stray pieces on the sand easily.

2 Wear sturdy, rubber-soled shoes so you don't slip moving across any damp rocks.

3 Take pictures to record all the different types of seaweed you have found.

Score 20 eco points for taking pictures or recording your seaweed finds in a nature diary.

20 ECO POINTS

Amazingly, seaweeds are thought to be able to store large amounts of carbon from the atmosphere and so these 'seaweed forests' are helping combat climate change! When you next see a piece of seaweed on the beach, remember to send it some thanks for maintaining the clean air that we breathe and reducing the effects of global warming. Can you spot all these different types of seaweed?

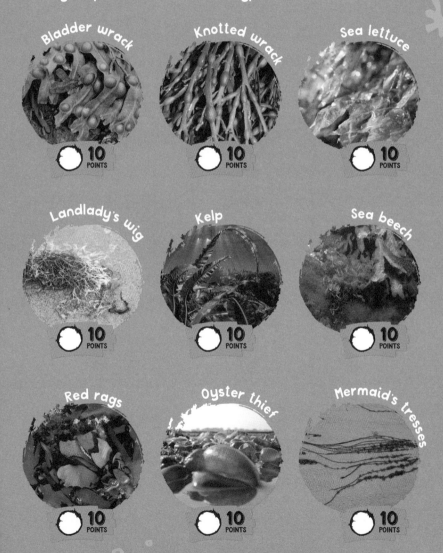

Bladder wrack
10 POINTS

Knotted wrack
10 POINTS

Sea lettuce
10 POINTS

Landlady's wig
10 POINTS

Kelp
10 POINTS

Sea beech
10 POINTS

Red rags
10 POINTS

Oyster thief
10 POINTS

Mermaid's tresses
10 POINTS

Jump over waves

Beaches can look drastically different over the course of the day due to the rhythm of the tide, which happens twice a day. Tides are caused by the gravitational force of the Moon and its pull on the water that make up our oceans. And so, the biggest differences between low and high tides occur around new and full moons.

One way to really see this concept in action is to visit the same area at the beach a few times over the course of a day and evening and make a note/take a picture how the tide has differed throughout your visits.

Another way to appreciate the tide is to take your shoes and socks off, roll up your trousers and jump over the waves rolling on to the beach.

Notice how quickly the tide recedes and washes back on to the beach – can you outrun it?

What does the wet sand feel like between your toes? How cold is the seawater?

Humans aren't the only animals that enjoy the waves —
many animals have been recorded surfing to catch food,
escape predators or simply just to play. Can you spot...?

Some species of jellyfish can
be found near the surface of
the ocean, riding the swell
of the waves up and down.

10 POINTS

Seal

Seals, like dolphins, are extremely social
and playful — many species all over
the world have been recorded surfing
through the ocean just for enjoyment.

15 POINTS

Sea duck

These birds can be seen surfing rough seas,
waiting for just the right moment when a
tide will carry in a crustacean before dipping
underwater and grabbing it for dinner.

20 POINTS

Dolphin

Dolphins not only enjoy
surfing alongside boats, but
some species also surf for
their food. They do this by
'hydroplaning', using their
bodies like a surfboard to
glide over shallow water
and snatch up fish who
are hiding there.

TOP SPOT!

30 POINTS

Dig a hole at the beach

Another classic beach activity is digging a big hole in the sand. If you are with friends or family, have a competition to see who can dig the biggest hole.

You'll need:

bucket, spade, sunscreen, hat

What to do:

1 If you are spending time in the sun digging your hole, always remember to wear plenty of sunscreen and a hat.

2 With your spade trace a circle in the sand where you will dig your hole.

3 Start to dig from the inside out, to stop your hole collapsing in on itself, and use your bucket to remove the sand well away from the hole.

4 If you dig your hole close to the tide, wait till the tide comes back in and watch it flood!

5 Always make sure a grown-up is close by to watch over you.

Lots of animals at the beach can be found digging in the sand too. Can you spot...?

Sand hopper

These crustaceans live up to their name as they are able to jump high into the air when disturbed. They spend their days buried in sand to hide from predators, only emerging at night to feed on seaweed.

10 POINTS

Razor shell

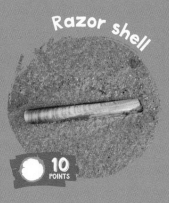

Razor shells or razor clams are a burrowing species living in sand around the low tide mark across UK beaches.

10 POINTS

Harvestmen

These spider-like invertebrates are found commonly on the beach hunting for sand hoppers.

15 POINTS

Sand mason worm

This worm can be seen all over UK coasts and builds its tube-like home out of sand and bits of shell. The worm and most of the tube is buried in the sand with just the top of the tube sticking out.

20 POINTS

Go surfing

Surfing is a fun physical activity for all ages and, by balancing on a surfboard, it gives you an appreciation of the movement of waves and swells of the sea. It is a great way to spend an afternoon at the beach. If you are a first-time surfer, have a lesson with a surf school, which will be able to give you top tips and safety advice.

You'll need:

surfboard, wetsuit

What to do:

1 Scope out the area where you want to surf – you want ideal weather conditions (not windy) and to know if the tide is in or out.

2 When the conditions are just right, and an adult can supervise you, change into suitable clothes for surfing and take your board down to the beach.

3 Be respectful of other surfers and never steal someone else's wave.

4 Find your balance before paddling out into the ocean.

5 When a wave is clear of others and you have found your balance, wait for the right moment as the wave rolls underneath your board, and then stand up tall in one smooth burst and surf the sea all the way back to shore!

Many people enjoy doing water sports at the beach.
Can you spot the following?

Surfer
10 POINTS

Bodyboarder
10 POINTS

Jetskier
15 POINTS

Windsurfer
15 POINTS

Kitesurfer
20 POINTS

Wakesurfer
30 POINTS

TOP SPOT!

Explore a cave

Exploring a cave is known as 'spelunking'. Coastal caves form when waves force their way into cracks in the side of cliffs. The seawater carries debris such as sand, which grinds away at the rock until the cracks become a cave. Eventually, the water will erode through the opposite side of the rock to create an arch and, over time, the top of the arch will collapse due to the force of the waves and weather.

You'll need:

a guide, head torch, warm clothing, sturdy shoes

What to do:

1. Large caves can be explored safely through organisations or guides who will know the best time of day and correct weather conditions to visit.

2. When exploring a cave, you should dress appropriately in warm clothing and supportive, sturdy shoes as the ground can be uneven and rocky.

3. A head torch may be beneficial to help see into dark and gloomy corners or view high cave ceilings.

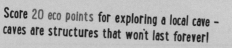

Score 20 eco points for exploring a local cave – caves are structures that won't last forever!

20
ECO
POINTS

Caves form over a long period of time and throughout history humans have used them for shelter, as burial sites and for religious purposes. When exploring a cave, can you spot these features?

Speleothems are cave formations created by minerals left in caves through the movement of water. Formations which hang from caves like icicles are called stalactites and those that emerge from the ground are called stalagmites.

stalactites

10 POINTS

stalagmites

10 POINTS

Troglobites are small creatures that have adapted to a permanent life in a cave and would not be able to survive outside. Troglophiles are animals that choose to spend their life in caves (but could survive outside of them too) and include some species of spiders, insects, fish and reptiles. Due to caves being dark many of these animals have lost the ability to see and are pale in colour as they do not need protection from the sun.

Cave spider   Springtails   Pink woodlouse

10 POINTS   10 POINTS   10 POINTS

Make a sundial in the sand

A sundial is a device which tells the time of day when there is sunlight from the position of the Sun in the sky. Historians believe the first sundial was created over 1,000 years ago by the Egyptians. Now many people have watches and mobile phones to tell the time, but sundials are often still used as decorative pieces in parks and gardens.

Why not create your own sundial in a place that is typically flat and receives a lot of sunshine – the beach!

You'll need:

spade, bucket, lots of small sticks, one long stick, 12 large shells or pebbles

What to do:

1 Pick a sunny day where there are minimal clouds in the sky, so you receive maximum exposure to your sundial.

2 Find a flat area of a sandy beach that is less likely to be disturbed by passers-by or dogs. Arrive as early as possible to get the full use of your sundial.

3 Using your bucket, collect lots of small sticks and when you have enough, use them to outline a large circle in the sand.

4 With your spade, smooth out the sand inside the circle of sticks – this will be the face of your sundial.

5 Place a long stick (the longer the better) in the middle of your circle.

6 At the top of each hour mark on the face of your sundial the location the shadow from the centre stick casts with an item such as a large stone or stick.

7 Watch throughout the day as the position of the shadow moves around the sundial.

How does it work?

Where the Sun is in the sky will determine where the shadow line on your sundial will appear. During the middle of the day, the Sun will be high in the sky, and the line from the stick's shadow will be short. As the day goes on and the Sun gets closer to the horizon the shadow will get longer.

A shadow is cast when an object blocks the sunlight – the sundial stick stops the sunlight reaching the area of ground it is above, so beneath the stick appears dark.

It may look like the Sun is moving across the sky but in fact it is the Earth that spins, as our planet rotates one complete circle every day.

Search for buried treasure

Do you ever wonder what treasures could be buried beneath the sand? When visiting a beach, searching for long, lost relics with a metal detector isa fun way to spend the day.

You'll need:

metal detector, spade, notepad and pen, patience!

What to do:

1 To search for treasure efficiently, you will need a metal detector. Buy, rent or borrow one to use at your day at the beach or even join a local metal detecting club.

2 Check with an adult that you have permission to use your metal detector in the search area.

3 Searching for treasure is best done when the beach isn't crowded so aim for an early morning start. It is easier to find items in areas of soft, dry sand.

4 Plan a search area and make a note of it in a diary – this helps you keep track of where and when you carried out searches.

5 If your metal detector alerts you to an item in the sand, use your spade to dig it out.

6 Record everything you find in your diary.

Hunting for treasure along the beach may not always end in gold – you may come across a lot of junk items too. Score 30 eco points for binning the rubbish you find.

30 ECO POINTS

On your search, can you spot something...?

...shiny?

10 POINTS

...big?

10 POINTS

...round?

10 POINTS

...plastic?

10 POINTS

...colourful?

10 POINTS

...hard?

10 POINTS

Go crabbing

Crabbing is a great activity to do by a rock pool or on the side of a harbour in the sunshine.

You'll need:

fishing line, fishing rod, bait bag, bait such as bacon, bucket of seawater, fishing net, camera

What to do:

1 Ask an adult to help attach the fishing line to a suitable fishing rod or, if you don't have one, tie your line around a small, plastic spade that will act as a handle.

2 Add your bait to the bait bag. When you are ready to fish, tie some bait to the end of your fishing line.

3 Swing the end of your fishing line into the rockpool or sea. Be patient! Crabs may take some time to notice the bait so don't move your line around too much.

4 When a crab takes the bait, you may feel a sharp tug on the line. Wait a few seconds for it to get a good hold.

5 Slowly raise your fishing line out of the water and place the crab in your bucket (watch for its pincers).

6 Take a close-up picture of the crabs you caught, then carefully place them back where you found them.

Score 10 eco points for being kind to the crab – add rocks and seaweed, don't have too many crabs and don't keep them in there for too long.

10 ECO POINTS

There are many species of crab and other crustaceans that may be tempted by your baited line. Can you spot...?

Common prawn

A common sight in rockpools and shallow waters. the prawn has a translucent body with brown stripes.

10 POINTS

Edible crab

This crab is brown with black tipped pincers and likes to hide underneath boulders. Many restaurants serve them up for dinner!

10 POINTS

Velvet swimming crab

Known for its beady. red eyes and feisty nature. this crab is also known as the 'devil crab'. The short hairs covering its body give it a velvet appearance.

20 POINTS

Olive squat lobster

These crustaceans prefer to live in rocky shores and shallow waters. hiding under large stones. When disturbed they slap their tail and scoot backwards to escape.

20 POINTS

Scampi

TOP SPOT!

This small. orange lobster lives in self-dug burrows on the seabed. appearing mainly at night to feed on smaller crustaceans. worms and starfish.

30 POINTS

Go barefoot

Walking on the sand barefoot is not just a great form of exercise. but a good way to clear your mind and get in touch with nature through. not only what you see and hear. but how the ground feels underneath your feet too.

What to do:

1 Wear sunscreen in summer and make sure an adult is with you or knows where you are at all times.

2 Plan your route so you know how long your walk will take and how to get back to where you started.

3 Walking early morning or just before the Sun sets are often preferred times when it is less crowdy with people on the beach.

4 When walking. make a note in your head of how the sand feels. Is it hot? Soft? Are you spending some of your journey walking through the waves? How does it feel?

How does it help you?

- Walking barefoot tones your legs and can improve your circulation.
- The sand is a great exfoliator so walking across it removes the dead. hard skin on your feet leaving them super soft.
- Seawater contains lots of natural minerals. therefore walking through it gives your skin a mineral boost.

Your walk along the beach may incorporate different locations such as a promenade, harbour, dunes or beachfront. On your way, how many different textures do you feel under your feet?

Sand
5 POINTS

Seawater
5 POINTS

Grass
5 POINTS

Cobbles
5 POINTS

Cemented path
5 POINTS

Pebbles
5 POINTS

Wood
5 POINTS

Rocks
5 POINTS

Seaweed
5 POINTS

Go birdwatching at the beach

Humans aren't the only ones who enjoy visiting the beach – lots of birds spend a great deal of their day there too, so it is important we be mindful of the natural world on our holiday or on days out. Keeping a safe distance from wildlife, making sure dogs are kept on leads and tidying up after ourselves are some of the ways we can protect beaches.

You'll need:

binoculars, camera

What to do:

1 Choose your outfit – pick neutral colours to blend into the background and wear lots of sunscreen as you may be out in the sun for most of the day.

2 Choose your location – select a spot that's quiet and allows you a clear view of the sky and surroundings.

3 If taking pictures remember to turn the flash off on your camera as the sudden, bright light may scare birds.

4 Stay quiet and be patient – birds will come along eventually.

Can you spot any of these species of shore bird?

Ringed plover

A short-legged wading bird that enjoys snacking on marine worms, crustaceans and molluscs. These birds build nests on the ground amongst sand, shingle or gravel.

10 POINTS

Oystercatcher

If you hear a loud 'peep-ing' call early morning coming from the beach, it will most likely be from an oystercatcher as they scour the area for shellfish for breakfast.

10 POINTS

Cormorant

Even though these birds spend a lot of time in water their feathers aren't waterproof, so you can often see them perched on buoys or rocks drying off.

10 POINTS

Sanderling

Sanderlings visit the UK mostly through winter and are often seen chasing waves in their search for jellyfish and crustaceans to eat.

10 POINTS

Pied wagtail

These black and white birds get their name from the way they often bob their long tail up and down. They can be seen not just on beaches, but in towns and cities too.

10 POINTS

Spot the difference between gulls

Did you know there is no such thing as a seagull? Gulls make up a large family of seabirds, but no one species is known as a 'seagull'. They are known for stealing chips at the seaside, but these birds are doting parents to their chicks and are quite intelligent.

It can be extremely difficult to identify gulls at the beach, but if you know what to look for you can spot the differences and impress those around you.

Herring gull

Large, noisy birds found scavenging on rubbish. Look out for: light grey backs with white underparts, black tipped wings with small, white spots and a slightly hooked yellow bill marked with a red spot. Young ones are mottled brown and white.

10 POINTS

Lesser black-backed gull

These birds tend to be slightly smaller than the herring gull. Look out for: dark grey back and wings with white underparts, yellow legs and a yellow bill with red spot.

10 POINTS

This species is the world's largest gull with a huge wingspan. Look out for: large, dark grey back and wings with white underparts, pale pink legs and a large, square head with a heavy, yellow bill marked with a red spot.

Great black-backed gull

15 POINTS

Common gull

These birds are like smaller versions of herring gulls without the hooked bill. Look out for: light grey backs with white underparts, black tipped wings with small white spots, yellow/green legs and a thin, pale, yellow bill.

15 POINTS

Very sociable birds, typically seen in small flocks that grow in number where food is available. They are a lot smaller than the herring or black-backed gull. Look out for: light grey backs with black-tipped wings which have a white edge, white underparts, dark pink legs and a dark brown/black head and bill.

Black-headed gull

20 POINTS

Kittiwake

Strictly coastal gulls often nesting on cliffsides and feasting on sandeels, kittiwakes are slightly larger than black-headed gulls. Look out for: light grey back and wings with black tips and white underparts, black legs and a small yellow bill.

30 POINTS

TOP SPOT!

Tie a sailor's knot

Sailing provides you with the opportunity to get close to marine life, can teach you about teamwork, and help you gain an understanding of how to use the wind and waves to move through the water.

Something that every good sailor should know is how to tie different knots. One common knot is the 'Savoy knot' or 'Figure eight knot'. Mastering this will impress even the toughest of sea captains!

What to do:

1 Grab a piece of rope and hold one end in one hand and the rest of the rope in the other hand.

2 Cross one end over the rope in your other hand, about halfway at its length, creating a loop shape.

3 Then wrap the end piece around behind the rope and pull forward and down into the loop shape.

4 Pull the rope end down and at the same time pull the rest of the rope in the other hand. You should now have a perfectly tight knot that is shaped like the number 8.

Listen to the ocean

Did you know you can hear the ocean
even when you are far from a beach?
It's true! Holding up a large shell to
your ear produces a sound just
like that of waves lapping up
on to the sand.

What to do:

Conch shells are the best
shells to use to hear the ocean.
They are indigenous to waters
around the Gulf of Mexico and the
Caribbean so it may not be easy
to find them, but any other large shell
will be fine. Once you have found the perfect shell, close
your eyes, and hold the opening of the shell up to one of
your ears. Can you hear the ocean?

How does it work?

Obviously, the ocean isn't in the shell you are listening to,
so what is producing the noise you hear? Scientists believe
the answer to this is the echo of the noise in the air around
you. This is known as the ambient noise. The shape of the
shell captures the ambient noise which then echoes inside it,
producing the kind of sound you hear at the beach.

Depending on the size and shape of the shell you use,
different frequencies of sound will be emitted. This means
different shells will make a different 'ocean noise'.

Collect different shells at the beach you visit and compare
what sounds the best!

Look out for jellyfish

There are thousands of species of jellyfish and around the UK large blooms of them can be seen in waters from spring through to autumn. When exploring the beach and out at sea can you spot any of these? Don't touch though, as some can sting!

Barrel jellyfish

The UK's largest jellyfish, which can be seen all year round and looks like a huge, translucent mushroom with eight frilly tentacles.

 10 POINTS

Moon jellyfish

10 POINTS

One of the most common jellyfish found around the UK and known for its transparent, umbrella body, through which you can see four purple circles. It has hair-like tentacles.

Typically yellow or off-white in colour and takes the shape of a bell as it drifts through the ocean. This jellyfish also has brown 'V-shaped' markings on its dome and around the fringe of the bell.

Compass jellyfish

10 POINTS

Mauve stinger jellyfish

TOP SPOT!

30 POINTS

Fairly rare in the UK, this colourful jellyfish has long, strand-like tentacles that can reach 3 metres in length. They can have pink, purple or yellow colouring.

Play 'stones and shells'

It's fun to break up exploring nature at the seaside or relaxing and sunbathing with a good dose of healthy competition. Try this beach version of noughts and crosses!

You'll need:

2 or more players, a stick, 5 stones and 5 shells found on the beach

What to do:

1 Each player searches the beach for counters to play with. One should find 5 stones, while the other player should find 5 shells.

2 Draw out the 'board' on the sand using a stick, forming a 3x3 grid as shown in the photo.

3 The youngest of the players starts by putting one of their items in a square on the 'board'. Then the next player takes their turn.

4 Each plays until someone gets three in a row of their item (vertically, horizontally or diagonally).

5 If playing with more than two players, the winner plays against a new opponent.

Have a picnic

Pack a picnic of delicious food to eat at the seaside. Find a beautiful spot, and hope that the weather stays fine!

You'll need:

picnic blanket, picnic basket and/or cool box, drinks containers, plates, cutlery, food and drink

What to do:

1 Plan all the ingredients you'll need to make your picnic lunch and get shopping!

2 Prep your food – sandwiches and fruit always make a great selection for outdoor eating.

3 Pack your picnic basket and/or cool box.

4 Don't forget sunscreen, to safe day in the sun.

5 Pick a flat, quiet area and enjoy the company of family or friends, and the food you prepared.

Score 20 eco points if you tidy up after yourself and don't feed wildlife any leftovers – it can attract rodents to the area which are a danger to ground nesting birds.

20 ECO POINTS

Can you spot any of the following things while having your seaside picnic?

Sunscreen
5 POINTS

Hot air balloon
30 POINTS

Strawberry
5 POINTS

Parasol
5 POINTS

Kite
5 POINTS

Ice lolly or ice cream
5 POINTS

Frisbee
5 POINTS

Beach warning flag
10 POINTS

Dog
5 POINTS

Be part of a beach clean-up

Be part of the fight against plastic and pollution by taking part in a beach clean-up. Find a local organisation who carry out beach clean-ups or organise one yourself.

You'll need:

hi-vis vest, litter picker, gloves, strong bin bags

What to do:

1 Pick a warm, dry day and an area of the beach you want to litter pick.

2 If organising your own beach clean-up, why not draw posters advertising for others to get involved?

3 Wear suitable clothing to keep you protected from the weather and from the rubbish you collect.

4 Move along the beach as a group collecting any litter with your litter picker and placing it in your bin bags.

5 Contact your local authority to collect your filled bags or dispose of them at a waste and recycling centre.

Score 30 eco points for helping wildlife and the environment by keeping the beach clean!

30 ECO POINTS

Plastic, fishing lines and litter end up in our oceans and in turn wash up on our beaches, so taking the time to collect and dispose of it is an amazing way to help the planet. As you go, can you spot and bin the following items?

Plastic bottle
5 POINTS

Crisp packet
5 POINTS

Cotton bud
5 POINTS

Coffee cup
5 POINTS

Balloon
5 POINTS

Fast food packaging
5 POINTS

Hand wipe
5 POINTS

Face mask
5 POINTS

Fishing line
5 POINTS

Spot seaside animal homes

Lots of animals use the beach as a home, but different ones use different parts of it as shelter and to raise their young. When you're out and about at the seaside, keep an eye out for any kind of animal home – look for clues that might help you, like feathers, footprints and poo.

Can you spot these homes?

Puffin burrow

These 'sea parrots' spend their winters at sea before returning to UK coasts to raise chicks. Each pair will produce one egg which they will raise underground in a 'puffin burrow'. Their bills are serrated (jagged) to help them hold their food, such as sandeels, securely.

10 POINTS

Cliffs make great nest spots as predators, such as foxes, can't get to them. Seabirds such as razorbills, guillemots and fulmars nest on steep cliff ledges. Visiting these sites (usually by boat) is an experience as the noise, sight and smell of a large colony of nesting birds is staggering!

Cliffside nests

20 POINTS

Ground nests

The UK is home to many ground nesting birds – you may be able to see nests amongst the sand and shingle of little terns and ringed plovers. Their eggs are highly camouflaged to protect against predators such as gulls.

10 POINTS

Seal colony

During autumn and early winter seals in the UK will come ashore to breed. When visiting a seal colony always remember to keep your distance and leave dogs at home. Mother seals will leave the pups alone on land to fish, so it is normal to see pups on their own. If a seal does have an obvious injury however you can call British Divers Marine Life Rescue (bdmlr.org.uk).

20 POINTS

Otter on kelp beds

The European otter is an excellent predator and can be seen around wetlands, rivers and coasts where they raise their young in underground burrows called 'holts'. These elusive animals can be hard to spot, but if you are lucky, you may see one having a snooze on a bed of kelp.

TOP SPOT!

30 POINTS

Write a letter to protect your beach

When you hear negative things about the state of the planet and our environment, it may seem overwhelming. A good way to help with this is to channel your frustrations into doing something wonderful for local habitats and wildlife.

Write to your local MP and tell them how important clean beaches are to you. Ask them what they are doing to protect animal and plant life there. This will help you plan what you can do next to help your local environment.

What to do:

1 Find your local MP at this website: https://members.parliament.uk/FindYourMP

2 Your letter should be polite but let them know how important protecting the beach is to you.

3 In your letter ask your MP for a reply and remember to leave a contact email or address so they can do so.

4 If you don't want to write a letter, you can even contact them via social media with the help of a grown-up.

Score 10 eco points when you have completed and sent your letter.

10 ECO POINTS

Be mindful at the beach

Mindfulness is a great activity to do every day or whenever you feel sad, bored or angry. You can practise mindfulness by taking a moment from your day, close your eyes and pay attention to what is happening in the present moment.

Being mindful at the beach is a calming experience as there are lots of things to focus on – the soothing sound of the waves, birds calling or the ocean breeze on your face.

What to do:

1 Find a quiet spot on the beach and get yourself into a comfortable sitting position.

2 Close your eyes and take a moment to focus on what you hear, smell and feel. Is the sand soft under your legs? Can you smell the salt from the seawater?

3 Focus on your breathing. If your mind begins to wander, don't get frustrated, just calmly return your thoughts to your breath.

4 Mindfulness can be tricky when you first start practising it, so start by being mindful for a few minutes and then increase the time as you progress.

Mindfulness has been shown to decrease stress and improve concentration – it's always good to take a quiet moment for yourself.

Do beach yoga

Exercise outside is proven to boost our physical and mental health, so exercising at the beach is a great way to improve your day. One form of exercise that is especially fun to do with friends and family is beach yoga.

You'll need:

loose, comfortable clothing, a mat or blanket, water

What to do:

1 Exercising at the beach is best enjoyed early in the morning or in the evening when the weather is cooler.

2 Find a flat area of sand and lay your mat down.

3 Remove your socks and shoes and try these poses. Score points for spotting someone doing these poses or for doing them yourself.

Warrior 2

10 POINTS

This pose is kind of like pretending to be a surfer. Stand with your legs shoulder length apart and arms wide out. Twist your head and hips to face your right knee and bend that slightly forward (until your knee is in line with your toes) to support your weight. Hold for 15 seconds and repeat on the left side.

Stand at the back of your mat with feet hip length apart. Then, with your arms hanging loose in front of your body, roll your hips forward until your hands touch the ground beside your feet. With your weight spread evenly across your hands and feet walk your hands forward until you create an upside down 'V' shape with your body. Hold for 15 seconds.

Downward Facing Dog

10 POINTS

Locust

10 POINTS

Whilst in Downward Facing Dog pose, keep your hands planted on the ground and raise your head. Slowly drop your hips to the ground and straighten out your feet, so the tops of them lie on top of your mat. Lift your chest, shoulders and head up and backwards like you want your shoulder blades to touch your lower back. Lift your feet off the ground if you can. Hold for 15 seconds.

There are lots of other yoga poses you can learn, but mastering these three is a good start!

Be creative at the beach

Exercising at the beach is not the only way to relax and feel good. Getting creative can also help improve your mood and is just a fun way to spend some time either on your own or with friends and family.

Paint a picture

You'll need:

paper, paint, paintbrushes, cup, water

What to do:

1 Explore the beach and find the perfect view that you would like to draw or paint.

2 When you have your paint, paintbrushes and cup of water set up, start painting what you see.

3 Can you mix the colours of paint on your palette to match the landscape?

4 To start your drawing pick out the largest shapes in your view and use them as a guide to map out your painting.

5 Remember, if you are spending time in one spot in the sun drink lots of water and cover up well.

Create a beach display

A beach display allows you to inspect items you find at the seaside closely and save those wonderful memories forever through pictures and keepsakes.

You'll need:

bucket, tray, magnifying glass, camera

What to do:

1 With your bucket, explore the beach and collect any unusual items such as shells, bird feathers, washed up animal bones etc.

2 When you have finished collecting items from the beach, lay them out on a blanket or tray and with your magnifying glass identify what everything is – can you tell what feather comes from what bird? What types of shells have you collected?

3 Arrange the items into categories or simply in a collage of what looks nice. Use your imagination to create your own beach display for others to enjoy.

4 Take a picture of the scene or sketch out what you have created and appreciate each item you have picked up.

5 Once you have finished place everything back where you found it.

Collect pebbles

Collecting pebbles is a hobby many people indulge in and one of the best places to go to do this is at the beach. A pebble is a smooth rock that fits in the palm of your hand and has formed due to the constant erosive power of the sea.

Before you go off in search of pebbles ask an adult to help you check that the beach you are at doesn't have any rules about removing pebbles from that area – there are usually signs up telling you this information too.

What to do:

1 When you are searching for pebbles keep your wits about you. Don't get too close to cliff edges and watch your footing when walking across tough ground.

2 Bring a strong carrier bag or box to transport your collected pebbles in.

3 Keep a note of where and when you found your pebbles.

Pebbles come in all different colours, shapes and sizes and can be made of different types of rock. Can you spot pebbles made of...?

Granite
5 POINTS

Schist
5 POINTS

Limestone
10 POINTS

Flint
10 POINTS

Red sandstone
15 POINTS

Conglomerate
20 POINTS

Red serpentine
20 POINTS

Basalt
20 POINTS

Amber
20 POINTS

Document your beach trip

If you have had a really good day at the beach, why not spend some of your evening putting together a scrapbook and use items collected from the seaside to decorate?

You'll need:

large blank notepad, items from the beach, photos of your day, glue, pens, pencils

What to do:

1 Decorate the cover of your scrapbook with your name and even with shells or sand.

2 In your scrapbook write about what you loved at the beach, what you saw and heard, what the weather was like and anything interesting that happened.

3 Stick on to the pages any items you collected with notes about what they are and where you found them.

4 If you took any photographs during the day leave room to stick those in too.

5 Keeping a scrapbook of you holidays or days out is a great memento and something you can look back on to remember your lovely day even years later!

Score 10 eco points for using a scrapbook made of recycled paper and decorating it with natural materials.

10 ECO POINTS

Bottle sand

Another easy to make keepsake is a glass bottle
or jar filled with sand from your favourite beach.
This thoughtful souvenir also makes a lovely gift
for a family member or a friend.

You'll need:

sand, glass bottle or jar with lid, ribbon,
items to decorate, gift tag

What to do:

1 At the beach, scoop some
sand into your bottle or
jar. If it is large enough
add items in the container
to decorate.

2 If your bottle of sand is a
gift, close your eyes and
make a wish on the bottle
for the person who it is
being gifted to.

3 Tie the ribbon and gift
tag around the top of the
bottle/jar and write a
message which explains
why the beach where you
collected the sand is your
favourite.

Go on a coastal walk

A walk near the sea is an unforgettable experience with spectacular views of waves crashing against rocks, nesting seabirds and dotted beautiful colours of coastal flowers. The UK has some very pretty coastal walks. What are you waiting for?

You'll need:

sturdy walking shoes, waterproof clothing, backpack, water, snack, camera

What to do:

1. Thoroughly plan your walk with the help of an adult and choose a day with calm, warm weather.

2. Pack extra clothing, a snack and plenty of water to keep you comfortable on your walk.

3. Take pictures with a camera of your favourite views and wildlife spots, but be aware of your surroundings at all times.

4. Make sure you are home before dark and take your time going up and down steep hills.

5. You may not come across a bin very often on your walk, so always store your litter in a pocket of your backpack until you can dispose of it properly.

Score 10 eco points for sticking to designated paths on your walk. This will avoid disturbing wildlife and damaging the area next to the path.

10 ECO POINTS

Learn about some flower species you may come across on your coastal walk. Can you spot...?

Sea campion

A seaside plant which grows on cliffsides and blooms between June and August. Recognised by its pretty, white flowers and distinctive green, fleshy leaves.

10 POINTS

Sea holly

This plant can be found amongst sand dunes across England and Wales. Despite its name and jagged leaves it's not related to the holly associated with Christmas.

20 POINTS

Thrift

Usually found on coastal cliffs, this plant is also known as 'sea pink'. Pretty pink clumps of thrift can be found across the UK, blooming between April and July.

10 POINTS

Sea beet

The ancestor of beetroot that we know and eat, this plant has green flowers on spikes. It can be spotted amongst shingle and even growing out of the side of cliffs.

20 POINTS

Golden samphire

In late summer this plant blooms on cliffs and rocky areas around the shore. Often seen growing amongst thrift, the florets are quite short and tend to stick upwards rather than outwards at first.

20 POINTS

Read a book at the beach

The beach is a naturally relaxing place, so it's a great place to catch up on some summer reading. Whether you like books about magic, lost treasure or aliens, you'll be able to get lost in the story under the sun.

Tips for reading at the beach:

- Bring a book to the beach that will take you all morning or afternoon to read and one that will keep you turning the pages to find out more.

- If using an e-reader remember to charge your device before leaving for the beach.

- Remember to wear sunscreen and bring sunglasses to protect you from the sun as you lay sprawled on the sand.

- Bring along a small cushion to keep your neck comfy whilst reading.

- The beach can be breezy and you don't want pages blowing in the wind when you are trying to read. Think about bringing a book weight with you to stop you losing your page.

Hold your breath

We breathe air in and out through our lungs, but other animals have different modes of breathing. Fish have gills and insects breathe through small openings along their bodies called spiracles.

Marine mammals need to be able to hold their breath for long periods of time in order to hunt. The elephant seal can do so for up to 2 hours!

How long can you hold your breath underwater?

You'll need:

goggles, stopwatch, notepad, pen

What to do:

1 Always make sure an adult is with you when you are doing this.

2 Practise holding your breath out of water first to get used to the feeling.

3 Find a shallow section of water and spend a minute or so breathing in and out slowly.

4 When you are ready, put on your goggles, take a deep breath and lower yourself under the surface of the water.

5 Very slowly breathe out bubbles through your mouth (this eases the pressure on your lungs) and ask the adult supervising to use a stopwatch to keep count of how long you stay underwater.

6 Keep a note of your times and see how quickly they improve.

Swim in the sea

Swimming in the sea is very different from swimming in a pool as you need to be aware of currents and tides, but once you know how to do so safely, it is a fun and unforgettable experience. Wild swimming has great health benefits and can also boost your mood. Only go if you have a grown-up with you.

Things to remember:

- Before going for a swim in the sea, you should think about where the best beach is to do so. Flat, shallow beaches, rather than ones that slope, are more suitable. The beach should ideally have a lifeguard and information about tide times.

- You will also want to swim where the water is clean. Blue flags indicate high water standards – they're the best places to take a dip.

- Waters around the UK tend to be cold all year round but are slightly warmer between July and August. If swimming outside of these months, using a wetsuit is a good idea.

- Always make sure an adult knows where you are and never go swimming alone.

- To make the most of your experience of swimming in the sea, go during a sunrise or sunset and watch how the sun glistens off the surface of the water. It's magical!

When you are swimming or snorkelling in the sea, can you spot these fish?

Cuckoo wrasse

These fish have slim, streamlined bodies with a pointed snout. Male fish have bright blue and orange markings, whereas the females are a pale pink. They prefer shallow, rocky areas.

20 POINTS

Sandeel

These long-lived animals are not actually eels, but fish, and eat mainly plankton. They can often be found buried in the sand of the seafloor where they hide from predators such as puffins.

20 POINTS

Lesser weever fish

Also spending a great deal of time buried in the sand, if disturbed these fish can inject a painful poison into unsuspecting predators through their dorsal fin.

20 POINTS

Butterfly blenny

This fish has a large, dorsal fin that extends down the length of its body and is a brown/grey colour. It mainly filters plankton from the water, but will also eat small crabs and worms.

TOP SPOT!

30 POINTS

Do a freshwater and saltwater experiment

Saltwater is denser than freshwater because of the salt content. See what happens when you mix them together.

You'll need:

2 glass beakers or jars,
2 smaller clear containers, salt,
tablespoon, blue and green food
colouring, dropper, labels, marker

What to do:

1 Label jars 1 and 3 'freshwater' and jars 2 and 4 'saltwater'.

2 Half fill jars 1 and 2 with water from the tap. Add a tablespoon of salt to jar 2, stirring until it has dissolved.

3 Pour some saltwater from jar 2 into jar 3 and add two drops of green food colouring.

4 Pour some freshwater from jar 1 into jar 4 and add two drops of blue food colouring.

5 With a clean dropper, add drops of the green saltwater (jar 3) to your clear freshwater (jar 1). Then add drops of the blue freshwater (jar 4) to your clear saltwater (jar 2).

6 What happens to the saltwater added to the freshwater? Do they eventually mix? How long does it take?

Watch a sunset

Sunsets are beautiful to watch and a great way to end a fantastic day on the beach. Grab some friends and family and settle down to witness one of nature's most spectacular shows.

What to do:

1. Choose a relatively clear day, although you may witness a more stunning effect if there are some clouds for the sunlight to bounce off.

2. Find a spot on the beach with a view to the west as the Sun will start to set in that direction.

3. Check what time the Sun sets in your area. The best time to watch is between 30 minutes before and 30 minutes after sunset.

4. Bring with you blankets and some hot drinks as once the Sun has set the temperature may begin to drop.

5. Don't stare directly at the Sun as it will damage your eyes.

6. Notice how different the colours of the sky are when the Sun is going down. During a sunset the sky will tend to turn shades of orange, pink and red. This is because, as the Sun approaches the horizon, the sunlight passes through more of the atmosphere. This scatters the blue light that we see in the day leaving only the red light.

7. See if you can spot any birds starting to roost. The fading light signals to birds to find a place to rest for the night.

Find out about basking sharks

The basking shark may look like something from the movie *Jaws*, but there is no need to fear this gentle giant as it filter feeds solely on small sea creatures known as zooplankton.

Basking sharks grow up to 11 m in length and are the second biggest fish in the oceans, coming second to the massive whale shark. They can be seen during summer in waters around Cornwall, the Isle of Man and the Inner Hebrides. You are most likely to see them up close by taking a boat trip with a reputable wildlife watching organisation.

TOP SPOT!

40 POINTS

Score 20 eco points for reporting a basking shark sighting to your local wildlife trust (see wildlifetrusts.org). They are an endangered species, and this will help conservationists learn more about them and how they can protect them.

20 ECO POINTS

You may not think it, but UK waters are home to many species of shark. Can you spot...?

Spiny dogfish

10 POINTS

This small, slender shark is grey with white spots and grows to between 60 and 120 cm long. It gets its name from the spines found in front of its dorsal fin.

Porbeagle shark

20 POINTS

You are very unlikely to see a great white shark around the UK, but its cousin the porbeagle shark is very active and can be seen all year round.

Angelshark

30 POINTS

The angelshark may look more like a ray than a shark with its flattened, diamond-shaped body and eyes on top of its head, but its ambush technique when catching prey is definitely more like its close shark relatives.

Thresher shark

50 POINTS

TOP SPOT!

This shark can reach up to 4 m long and is recognisable due to its large tail fin. It uses this like a whip to separate fish from shoals and stun them, making them easier to catch.

Find a mermaid's purse

Finding a mermaid's purse washed up on the beach is an exciting discovery and if you do always let your local Wildlife Trust know. But what exactly is it? These leathery pouches are the egg cases of sharks and rays.

Many species of shark and ray lay their eggs by attaching them to seaweed. The eggs can stay there for up to a year with the young fish developing inside. Once they leave the egg, the casing can often be found washed ashore, typically breaking off from the seaweed after a storm.

What to do:

1 The best place to find a mermaid's purse is at the high tide line as that is where they will end up after being washed up on the sand.

2 Long bands of seaweed stretching across the beach usually indicate the high tide line.

3 It is amongst the seaweed where you will have the best chance to find an egg casing, but look carefully, it can often look very similar to the seaweed it is attached to.

4 The next best place to find one is in rock pools. The mermaid's purse can quite often get trapped in there once the tide goes out.

Mermaid's purse

TOP SPOT!

30 POINTS

Watch bioluminescent plankton

Another of nature's spectacular light shows is that of bioluminescent plankton which turns the night time ocean into a sea of sparkling blue stars. Bioluminescence describes the light that some living creatures (also including jellyfish and fireflies) emit from special cells in their bodies.

What to do:

1 Research where to go for a chance to see this phenomenon. It usually occurs in warm, coastal waters abroad, but can sometimes be seen around the UK, especially in summer.

2 Have patience! Blooms of bioluminescent plankton are difficult to predict as they tend to occur far out in the ocean. However, tidal currents sometimes cause them to be washed closer to shore.

3 The plankton only emit light during the night when it is dark so, with permission from an adult, plan an evening excursion to the beach.

4 Remember to wear warm clothes as it may be cooler on the beach when the Sun has gone down, and you may have to wait a long time before you see anything.

Bioluminescent plankton

40 POINTS

TOP SPOT!

Camp on the beach

Camping on the beach is something that everyone should do at least once. There is no better feeling than camping out to the sound of the ocean, under a big blanket of twinkling stars.

You'll need:

tent, sleeping bag, firewood, food and drink, torch

What to do:

1 Once you have a good camping spot on the beach in mind, ask an adult to help you check if you have permission from the landowner to do so.

2 Check the tide times – if you don't, you may be woken up in the middle of the night by the incoming tide!

3 Pitch your tent and organise your sleeping bag before it gets dark, so you can see exactly what you are doing.

4 If making a fire do so safely and leave no trace after you have finished. Many beaches where camping is allowed have designated fire pits already set up.

5 Use a torch to get around. Lots of animals emerge from their burrows or homes after dark so be careful not to disturb anything when walking across the beach.

6 Spend your evening with family and friends telling stories, eating snacks and watching the stars – you will make wonderful memories.

Score 20 eco points if you leave no trace of your camping trip when packing up the next morning.

20 ECO POINTS

There are lots of different things to see and do when camping on the beach. Can you spot all of these?

Moon
5 POINTS

Marshmallows
5 POINTS

Campfire
5 POINTS

Driftwood
5 POINTS

People singing around a campfire
5 POINTS

Stars
5 POINTS

Backpack
5 POINTS

Torch
5 POINTS

Sleeping bag
5 POINTS

Make a time capsule

It's always good to look back on happy memories, after all that's why we take photographs and keep a diary. Putting together a time capsule is a great activity to do which allows you to reflect on fun moments in the past and think about what memories are important to you.

Beach holidays make great memories as you are spending time outside with friends and family – why not include something of that time in your time capsule?

You'll need:

waterproof and airtight box, paper, pen, items that are important to you, shovel

What to do:

1 Write a letter to your future self about what you hope to have achieved in life and how you feel at that very moment. Write down stories of your fondest memories too. Sign and date your letter, and add it to the box.

2 Think about what items you want to add. Objects such as shells, pebbles or a bottle of sand from your favourite beach make great keepsakes. You should fill up the container with items that, when you open it in the future, will make you smile.

3 Decide in what year you want to unearth your time capsule. It could be in 10, 20 or 50 years!

4 Find an area in your garden that is suitable to bury a large object. With help from an adult dig a deep hole in the ground to keep your time capsule in.

5 Cover it up and make a note of precisely where you have buried it – so it is easy to find in the future.

It may be hard to think about what objects are best to include in your time capsule. Having a chat with an adult about what to add or looking up what other people have done may help you. Here are some ideas of items you could add...

Something old

Something with a date on it

Something handwritten

Something personal

Something nostalgic

Something which captures a moment in time

Something that reminds you of a place

Something that will make you smile

Go fossil hunting at the beach

Collecting fossils is a fascinating activity and beaches around the UK are covered in items from the past – you just need to know where to look! Some good places to hunt for fossils include the Jurassic Coast (along the English Channel), Penarth in Wales, Danes Dyke in Yorkshire, and St Andrews in Scotland.

You'll need:

sturdy footwear, warm clothing, clear plastic bags/tubs, newspaper

What to do:

1 Plan your fossil hunting trip for the winter, when beaches are quieter and the fossils more plentiful due to severe weather causing more erosion to cliffs and rocks.

2 Look up tide times and search the beach when the tide is out.

3 Be careful walking over large pebbles and rocks – wear sturdy shoes that support your ankles.

4 Wrap up any fossils you find in newspaper to keep them safe before storing them in clear bags or tubs.

Many fossils simply lie exposed on the beach just waiting to be discovered. Can you spot any of these?

Seashell fossils

Looking similar to modern shells you would see on the beach, seashell fossils are more common than other fossils because the shell is hard and therefore more likely to be preserved.

10 POINTS

Ammonite

Related to octopus and squid, it is thought ammonites died out around 66 million years ago. They can be found in various sizes, most commonly after a storm.

10 POINTS

Belemnites

These fossils are the internal, hard part of a squid-like animal that also went extinct around 66 million years ago.

20 POINTS

Bones of Ichthyosaur

TOP SPOT!

The Ichthyosaur is an extinct marine reptile and its scattered backbones can sometimes be found along the Jurassic Coast.

50 POINTS

Find life in the sand

Life can be found all over the beach and surrounding area.

Sand dune dwellers

Sand dunes form above the high tide mark from mounds of sand which are often held together by grasses and plants. When exploring a sand dune can you spot...?

Pyramidal orchid

A small orchid that has bright purple flowers which form into a pyramid shape. It flowers in June and July and attracts a large variety of butterflies and moths.

10 POINTS

Digger wasp

Different from the kind of wasps commonly found in gardens, digger wasps are solitary insects with females making her own nest for her young.

20 POINTS

Sand lizard

TOP SPOT!

30 POINTS

Due to habitat loss this reptile is now a very rare sight around UK dunes. It is best glimpsed basking in the sun on the warm sand. Males turn a bright green colour in spring as they get ready to mate.

Hidden invertebrates

Many species of invertebrates (animals with no backbone) can be found hiding at the beach. Can you spot...?

Sand crab

Also known as 'mole crabs', these are a common sight at the beach. Typically found in groups, they prefer to stay shallowly buried in sand on the tide line. They feed on plankton caught in their antennae.

10 POINTS

Lugworm poo

Have you ever seen worm-like piles on the sand? They are caused by lugworms creating their U-shaped burrows by eating sand and then pooing it back out.

10 POINTS

Blood worms

These worms get their name from their bright red colouring. You may spot the tiny holes they make as they burrow into the sand.

20 POINTS

Orange clubbed sea slug

These 2-cm-long sea slugs are often found feeding on kelp on rocky shores. They lay thousands of eggs at a time which are attached onto seaweed and can be found all over UK coasts.

TOP SPOT!

40 POINTS

Have a bucket race

If you need to blow off some steam after sunbathing having a race is a good way to do so. The object of the bucket race is simple — to win!

You'll need:

2 teams of people, 2 same-sized buckets, 2 same-sized cups

What to do:

1 Divide a group of family and friends into two groups.

2 Ask the two teams to stand in a line beside each other on the beach about 30-40 metres from where the tide meets the sand.

3 Place a bucket down in the sand in front of each team. Give the first person in each team a cup each.

4 The first people in line have to run down to the water, fill up their cup with seawater and then run back to empty the water into their bucket. They then pass the cup to the nest person in the team and they do the same.

5 The winning team is the one that fills their bucket full of seawater first.

Fast animals at the seaside

Many animals need speed in order to catch food and to evade predators. Can you spot the following 'quick-movers'?

Octopus

The common octopus uses its eight tentacles, which are joined to its head, to capture and hold prey still, and also to propel itself through the ocean at high speeds.

10 POINTS

Squid

Squid are among the fastest invertebrates. Their eggs often wash up on the shore after stormy weather – look for groups of long, white, squishy objects on the beach.

20 POINTS

Swallow

These aerial acrobats are sometimes spotted around coasts, zipping across the ground as they catch insects on the wing. This migratory bird is a common visitor to the UK between April and October.

20 POINTS

Gannet

Gannets have a 2-metre wingspan and catch fish by plunging vertically into the sea. They dive at such speeds you can hear the smack when they hit the water from some distance away.

TOP SPOT!

30 POINTS

Fly a kite

Sea breezes make the beach the perfect place to fly a kite!

What to do:

1 Before flying your kite check the weather at the beach. Ideally you want a breezy day, but one that isn't too windy. Never attempt to fly a kite in heavy rain or lightning as this can be dangerous.

2 When you arrive at the beach and pick your spot, check the area is clear from any obstacles above you or on the ground.

3 Unwind the string of your kite about 3–4 metres and ask someone else to take the kite a few paces away.

4 Hold the string tight and when the wind is just right, ask the person holding the kite to run away from you and throw the kite into the air.

5 Notice the direction of the wind and adjust your position so you are in a straight line with the kite.

6 Unravel more string to send your kite higher into the air. Don't let go of the string!

7 Keep an eye on your kite, but always be aware of your surroundings on the beach, especially if it's busy.

Can you spot these different kinds of kite?

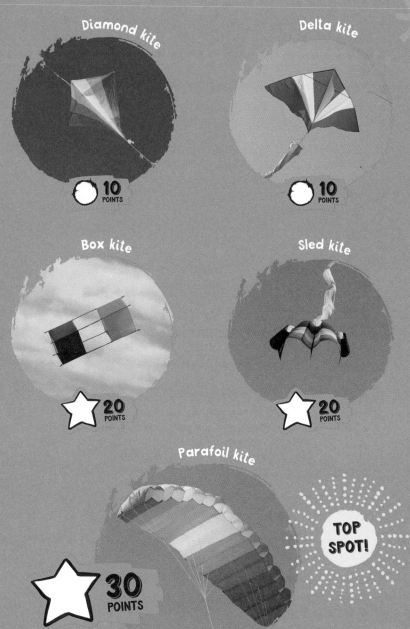

Diamond kite
10 POINTS

Delta kite
10 POINTS

Box kite
20 POINTS

Sled kite
20 POINTS

Parafoil kite
30 POINTS

TOP SPOT!

Reduce your carbon footprint at the beach

We should be mindful of the energy it takes to get us to the beach, and what we eat and use while we are there.

Here are some of the ways you could try to minimise your carbon footprint:

Instead of flying abroad for a beach holiday, try having one closer to home. Walk or cycle to the beach if you can, instead of driving there.

Re-use last year's summer outfits or buy second-hand clothes or those made from recycled materials.

When having a picnic on the beach eat seasonal products, e.g. strawberries and raspberries in summer, and only eat sustainably caught local fish.

Recycle as much of your waste as you can and try to avoid buying products with lots of plastic packaging.

Score 30 eco points if you minimise your carbon footprint by taking two or more of the actions above.

30 ECO POINTS

Renewable energy

Developing renewable energy sources is vital for our future and much better for the environment than burning fossil fuels. The wind, Sun and ocean can be powerful, clean suppliers of energy. Keep a look out for...

Wind turbines

10 POINTS

Often these huge turbine structures are found out at sea, using the ocean breeze to generate energy. They work almost like the opposite of an electric fan – instead of using electricity to make wind, the turbines spin in the wind and make electricity.

Solar panels

10 POINTS

Solar panels capture energy from the Sun. The panels absorb the energy and convert it to electricity that can be used to power houses and appliances.

Wave or tidal power

50 POINTS

Electrical energy is generated by harnessing the up and down motion of ocean waves. It is often produced by floating turbine platforms or buoys that rise and fall with the swells.

TOP SPOT!

Protect your local beach

Protecting the beach starts at home. When you flush an item not intended to be put in the toilet it can cause blockages, leading to waste from the sewage system ending up in rivers and on beaches. The pollution in our water can kill fish and cause severe harm to wildlife.

To protect your local beach never flush the following items:

- Wet wipes
- Cotton buds
- Nappies

- Dental floss
- Paper towels
- Medication

- Chewing gum
- Cooking oil
- Pet goldfish

Protect the beach declaration:

I promise to never flush the above items down the toilet and always protect beaches around the world.

Signed.. Date...

Score 30 eco points for signing the Protect the beach declaration.

30 ECO POINTS

When you are visiting the seaside, here are some ways to be a responsible beachgoer.

- Use organic sunscreen, or one with natural ingredients to reduce any nasty chemicals entering the ocean when you go for a swim.

- If you take your pet to the beach always make sure to pick up after them.

- Take part in the Great British Beach Clean: every September this week-long citizen science event sees hundreds of 'beach cleans' take place all round the UK.

There are a lot of groups and organisations that help protect beaches around the UK. Contact them to become a member, or to volunteer.

- Marine Conservation Society (www.mcsuk.org): this UK-based charity helps to protect coastlines and wildlife as well as raising awareness for cleaner, healthier oceans. Become a member, donate to local campaigns, and use their website to find out information about how to better protect beaches.

- Surfers Against Sewage (www.sas.org.uk): these ocean activists have local groups you can join and volunteer with all around the UK. Their goal is to rid the coastlines and oceans of plastic pollution and improve water quality for all.

- National Trust (www.nationaltrust. org.uk) and National Trust for Scotland (www.nts.org.uk): these trusts look after hundreds of miles of coastline around the UK. You can become a member to support their work. Visit their website to find out more about what they do.

Index

Take on the i-SPY nature challenge!

Discover more fun and fascinating
i-SPY books at collins.co.uk/i-SPY